I Love Bugs!

woolly bear

Some say the thicker a **woolly bear**'s black stripes, the colder the winter ahead.

millipede

Millipede means "1,000 legs," but most millipedes have around 230 legs.

grasshopper

The "ears" of a long-horned **grasshopper** are on its front legs, near its knees.

dragonfly

Dragonflies were around even before the dinosaurs!

beetle

Most **beetles**' wing covers are strong enough to hold several pounds.

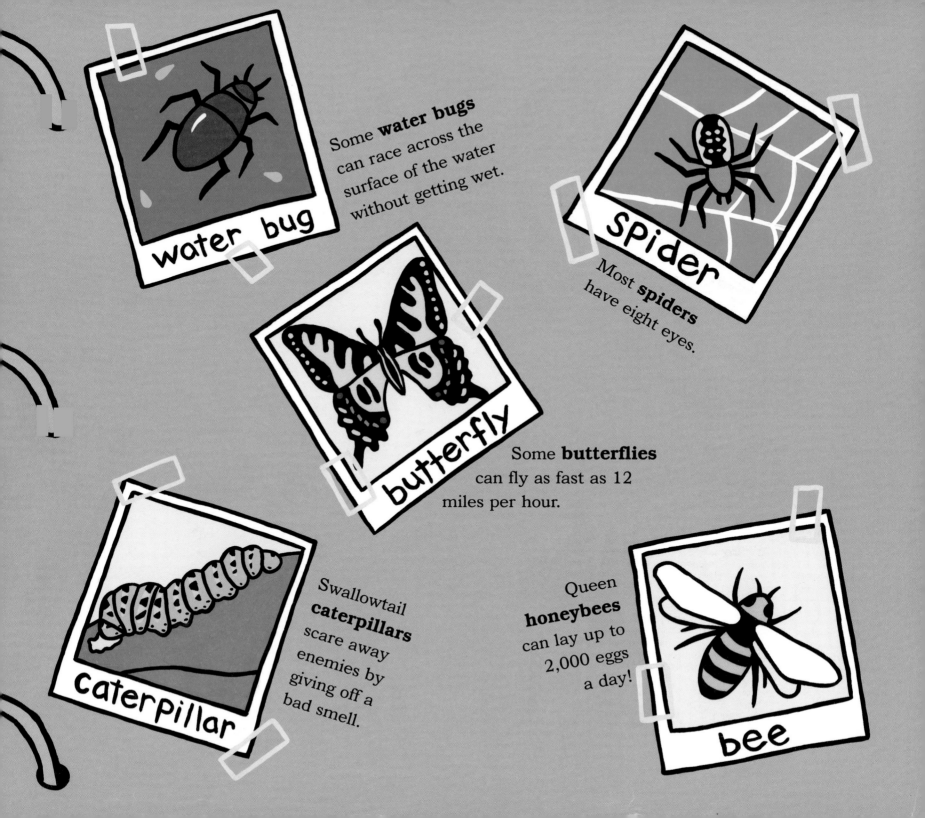

water bug

Some **water bugs** can race across the surface of the water without getting wet.

spider

Most **spiders** have eight eyes.

butterfly

Some **butterflies** can fly as fast as 12 miles per hour.

caterpillar

Swallowtail **caterpillars** scare away enemies by giving off a bad smell.

Queen **honeybees** can lay up to 2,000 eggs a day!

bee

To my three baby sisters,
Helen, Ronny, and Libby,
who never, ever, bugged me!
—P.S.

For my little bug,
Margaret Kate
—S.H.

ISBN 0-439-87504-8

Text copyright © 2005 by Philemon Sturges. Illustrations copyright © 2005 by Shari Halpern. All rights reserved. Published by Scholastic Inc., 557 Broadway, New York, NY 10012, by arrangement with HarperCollins Publishers. SCHOLASTIC and associated logos are trademarks and/or registered trademarks of Scholastic Inc.

12 11 10 9 8 7 6 5 4 3 2 1   6 7 8 9 10 11/0

Printed in the U.S.A.   40

First Scholastic printing, April 2006

I Love Bugs!

BY **Philemon Sturges**

ILLUSTRATED BY **Shari Halpern**

SCHOLASTIC INC.
New York Toronto London Auckland Sydney
Mexico City New Delhi Hong Kong Buenos Aires

Bugs, bugs, bugs! I like bugs.

Bugs that creep,

bugs that crawl,

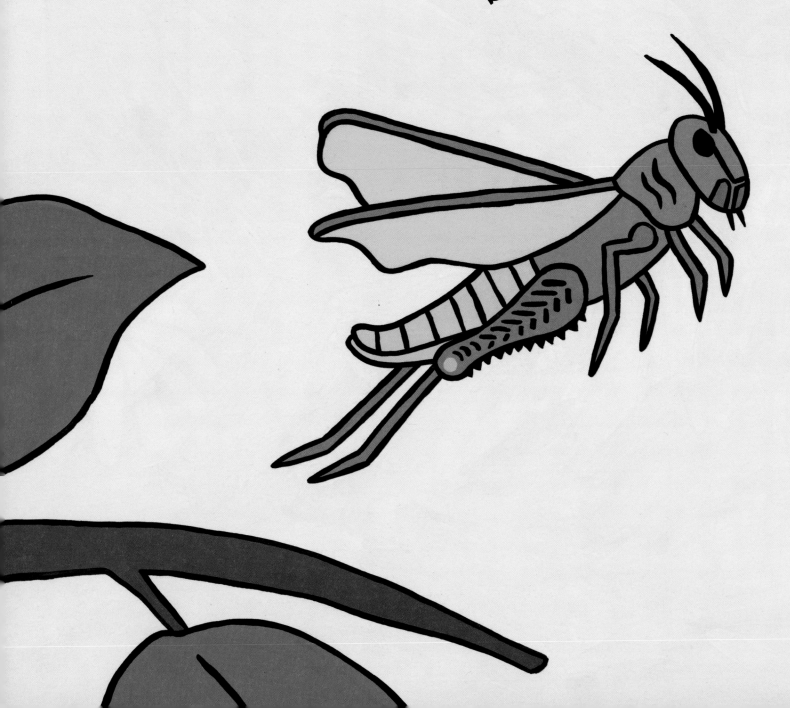

bugs that hop

or fly.

I love to find them under rocks

or watch them in the sky.

These bugs paddle.

This one weaves.

Some make honey.

Some chew leaves.

Some bugs burrow underground.

Others swoop and buzz around.

This one's like a bit of bark.

This one's like a twig.

Cicadas buzz a summer song.

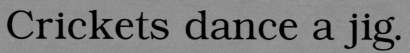
Crickets dance a jig.

I like bugs that blink at night

or flutter round the back porch light.

But this bug is the best of all.

It's Ladybug!

She loves to crawl.

Bugs, bugs, bugs! I LOVE bugs!

ant

Some **ants** can carry more than twenty times their own weight!

praying mantis

The **praying mantis** is the only insect that can turn its head halfway around to look over its shoulder.

cicada

Some **cicadas** spend seventeen years underground.

deerfly

The buzzing of a **fly** is the sound of its wings beating.

moth

Unlike butterflies, most **moths** are active at night.

The male **cricket** chirps by rubbing his front wings together.

cricket

Fireflies attract mates by blinking in special patterns.

firefly

Ladybugs can have from two to more than twenty-four spots.

ladybug

Luna moths have clear spots on their wings that you can see through.

luna moth

If a **baby sister** "bugs" you, it's just because she loves you!

baby sister